**mmmmm...my name is Marvin!**

**What would it be like
to sail far, far away,
down rivers and lakes
on a warm, windy day?**

**A south wind is blowing
as I study my chart.
Dreaming I'm on Lake Superior,
I'm ready to depart.**

Hoisting up my sail,
I'm going to the ocean.
I put on my sunglasses,
and Coppertone lotion.

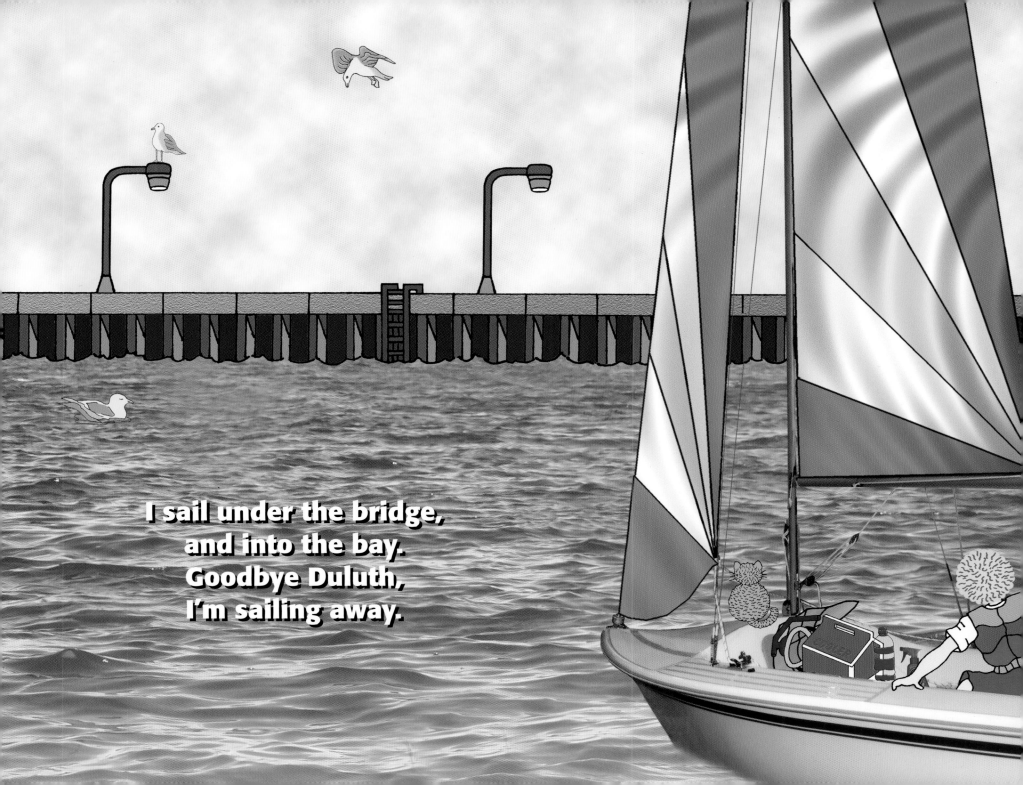

I sail under the bridge,
and into the bay.
Goodbye Duluth,
I'm sailing away.

MY LITTLE SAILBOAT

by Alice Palace

Bearpaw Books

I'm sailing to the ocean
so beautiful and blue.
What will I see,
and what will I do?

I see Split Rock Lighthouse
sitting high up on a rock.
What would it be like
to live up on top?

I'm sailing to the ocean
so beautiful and blue.
What will I see,
and what will I do?

Isle Royale is up ahead,
the island is a national park.
I see a moose on the shore,
by the woods so quiet and dark.

I sailed by Copper Harbor,
the town is friendly and small.
Then, I saw the Grand Hotel,
and the bridge by Mackinaw.

I saw some great big cities,
Detroit and Buffalo,
Niagara, Rochester, and Montreal,
and still some more to go.

I loved Lake Superior and Michigan,
Huron, Erie, Ontario and then, can it be true?
I finally reach the ocean,
so big, beautiful, and blue.

I sail down the coast,
and what do I see?
I see New York, New Jersey,
and the Statue of Liberty.

She welcomes our friends,
and now she sees me!
I just love America,
the land of the free.

I'm sailing the ocean
so beautiful and blue.
What will I see now,
and what will I do?

Oh, Oh! This is very scary,
I think I see a shark,
swimming behind me
in waters deep and dark!

He has beady little eyes,
and his fin stands up straight.
I know I can outrun him!
Mr. Shark, you're too late.

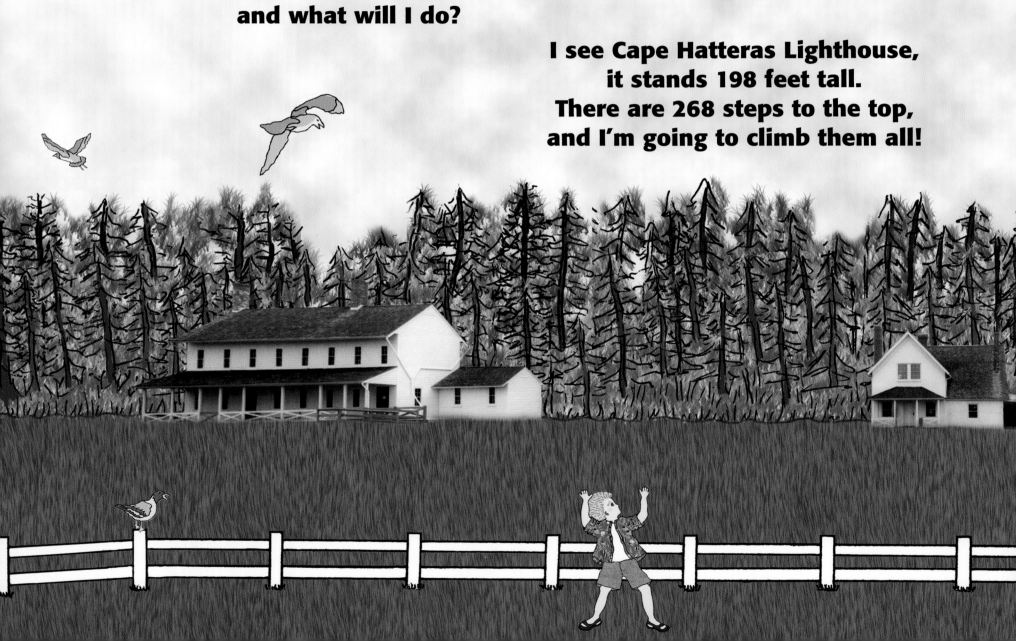

I'm sailing the ocean
so beautiful and blue.
What will I see now,
and what will I do?

I see Cape Hatteras Lighthouse,
it stands 198 feet tall.
There are 268 steps to the top,
and I'm going to climb them all!

I'm sailing the ocean
so beautiful and blue.
What will I see now,
and what will I do?

Catalina 16.5

I put on a snorkel,
and fins on my feet.
Jumping over the side,
I can't believe who I meet!

Friendly, gray dolphins
want to swim with me!
We dive into the waves
in the blue-green sea.

I'm sailing the ocean
so beautiful and blue.
What will I see now,
and what will I do?

Do you ever wonder
what flamingos think?
Which leg should I stand on,
and why am I so pink?

Wading in to join them,
I must be quite a sight!
Now, which leg should I stand on,
the left one or the right?

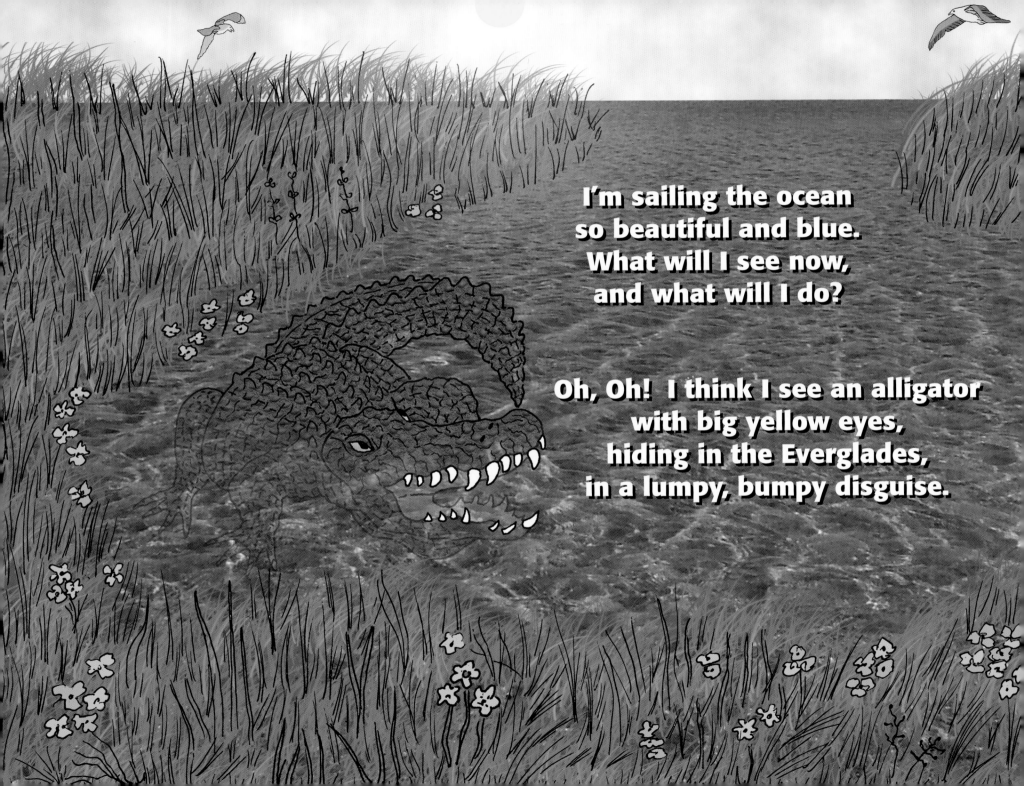

I'm sailing the ocean
so beautiful and blue.
What will I see now,
and what will I do?

Oh, Oh! I think I see an alligator
with big yellow eyes,
hiding in the Everglades,
in a lumpy, bumpy disguise.

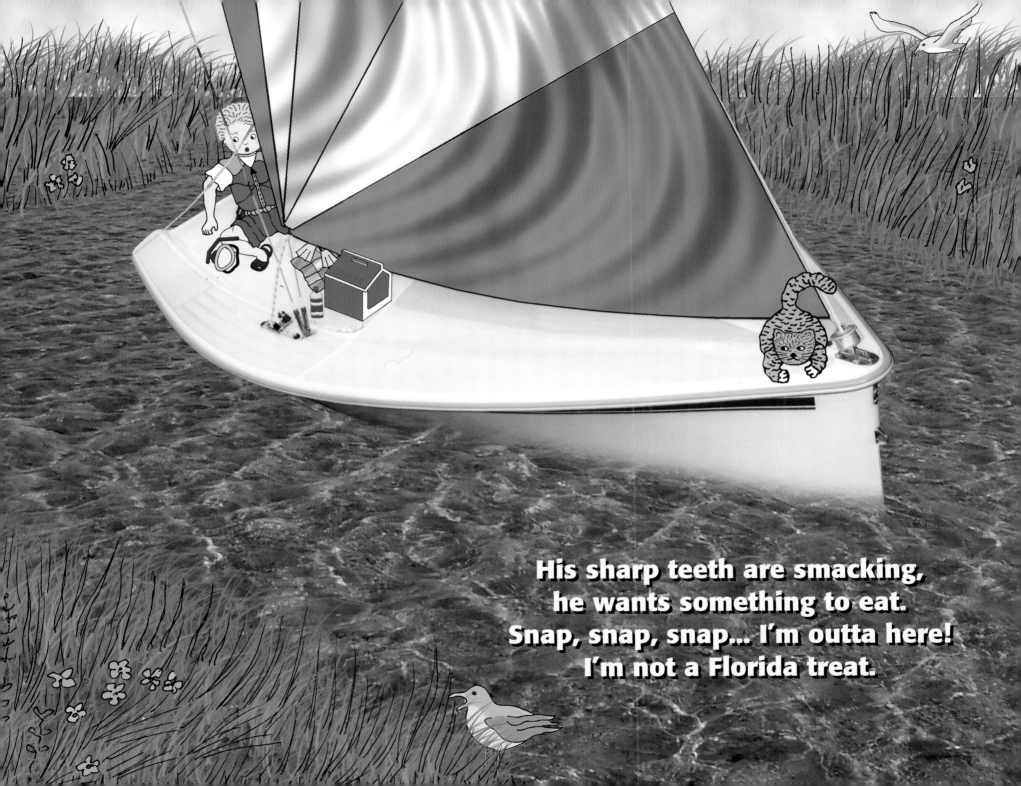

His sharp teeth are smacking,
he wants something to eat.
Snap, snap, snap... I'm outta here!
I'm not a Florida treat.

I see mama and baby manatee
floating down below.
Baby is cuddling mama,
and they're moving very slow.

Quietly I join them,
paddling by their side.
We swirl through the water,
enjoying the cool evening tide.

I'm getting very tired,
after sailing all this way.
It's time to go home now.
I had a wonderful day.

I sail into the Gulf,
and head to New Orleans,
go north at the Mississippi,
then up that mighty stream.

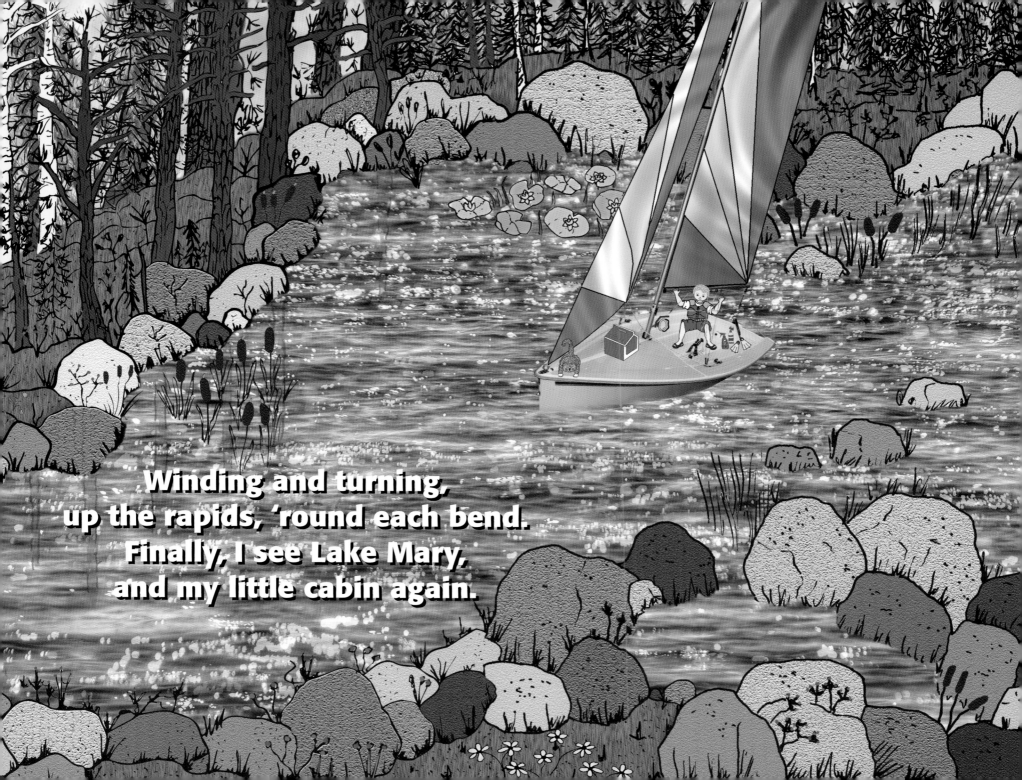

Winding and turning,
up the rapids, 'round each bend.
Finally, I see Lake Mary,
and my little cabin again.

I lower my sail, and
take down the boom.
I had a great vacation,
and never left my room!

It's time to go to sleep now,
I'll sail again someday.
So, good night ocean friends,
I'm glad we met today!

My Little Sailboat
Text and Illustrations Copyright 2007 by Alice Sizer
All Rights Reserved
ISBN 0-9709444-4-6

Graphic Design and Illustrations Colorized by Carrie Smeby
Creative Collaboration with Mary Anderson
Technical Assistance by Pamela Costello

A special thank you to:

Catalina Yachts
Woodland Hills, CA
www.catalinayachts.com

Isle Royale National Park
Isle Royale, MI
www.nps.gov/isro

Grand Hotel
Mackinac Island, MI
www.grandhotel.com

Schering-Plough HealthCare Products
Summit, NJ
www.sphcp.com

White Bear Boat Works
White Bear Lake, MN
www.whitebearboatworks.com

Cape Hatteras Light Station
Buxton, NC
www.nps.gov/caha
Michael Brindle, BrindlePix Photography
Bruce Roberts, Photographer

Split Rock Lighthouse
Two Harbors, MN
www.mnhs.org/places/sites/srl/

Statue of Liberty Club
Brian Snyder and Brenda Gale Beasley
Laurent Ghesquiere, Photographer
www.statueoflibertyclub.com

Jean-Paul Gaillard, Photographer

www.dreamstime.com, Photographers:
Wolfgang Amri • Elena Elisseeva
Eric Gevaert • Jimmy Lopes
Rob Marmion • Susan Mckenzie
Mark Snelson • Nick Stubbs

Sarasota Jungle Gardens, Sarasota, FL
www.sarasotajunglegardens.com

For more information contact:
Bearpaw Books
12 Ridge Road
St. Paul, MN 55127
www.bearpawbooks.com

Enjoy other books by Alice Palace:
Adventure One, *My Little Cabin* • Adventure Two, *My Little Lighthouse* • Adventure Three, *My Little Fish House*
Adventure Four, *My Little Pine River* • Adventure Five, *My Little Sailboat*

Printed and bound in the United States of America by Printing Arts, Brooklyn Park, Minnesota
Muscle Bound Bindery, Minneapolis, Minnesota